£4.50
HND

D0314370

Indian Head Massage

for

Absolute Beginners

Stephan Julian Radcliffe

©

Published by Lulu.com – 2010

Contents

Introduction

DISCLAIMER

For the purposes of this book, and as with other similar *written* material, it should be understood from the outset that a subject which is primarily administered through physical means, (treatments), further learning and appreciation should also be sought through 'practical' training. A suitable professional training course and the use of visual training aids such as a specifically focussed DVD is recommended. The author prefers that readers adopt a professional approach to the subject and that readers also understand the need to be recognised by further qualifications and professional organisations through which to uphold an ethical approach to and for the world of 'complementary' therapies.

It should be noted that upon completion of the reading of the material intended to form part or whole of *Indian Head Massage for Absolute Beginners*, the author has awarded no worldwide recognisable qualification, no diploma and no certificate of attendance. The information imparted in this material is intended to give readers a basic understanding of the subject and possibly to inspire the need for further additional learning. Initial interest in the subject is implied by the purchase of this material. Any treatments or advice offered by readers as a result of reading this material are administered at the sole responsibility of the reader. In case of any medical conditions, please seek the advice of a fully qualified medical practitioner, consultant, doctor or other suitably qualified professional *before* administering any of the techniques and / or treatments outlined in this introductory manual.

Introduction

Welcome to *Indian Head Massage for Absolute Beginners*. The aim of this book is to give you a basic step by step understanding into the relaxing and beneficial world of Indian Head Massage or IHM. It is a subject which is calming, wonderful, relaxing and much more besides and may help with the alleviation of many symptoms.

Everybody around the world can benefit from the amazing effects of the techniques that have been handed down from generation to generation and which offer human beings the opportunity of sharing in the tradition and therapies of many different cultures. We can connect with each other through the simple 'laying on' of hands which is considered to be one of the most instantaneous forms of healing.

By using easy to follow movements these will evolve into a whole treatment which will bring joy and happiness to friends, loved ones and the whole family and by appreciating effective techniques, we can easily learn how to apply these to bring about an array of relaxing treatments. Ultimately with Indian Head Massage we are attempting to change the flow of energy inside our mind, body and spirit which can make us feel better instantly and can have a profound effect on us as individuals.

We use simple movements and techniques along with the most suitable ambient surroundings to create a shift and 'rebalancing' which allows us to function better in our working lives, feel more content and become connected to all of life around us and our everyday lives can become enriched in wonderful ways whoever and wherever we are in the world.

One

The Growing Trend

The History of Indian Head Massage

The Role of Indian Head Massage

The Growing Trend

Before we begin to think about learning or offering any type of 'complementary' therapy, it is important to understand something about the origins of the treatment. Respectfully, this allows us not only to appreciate the therapy and practice but can also allow us the possibility to carry on the true tradition of the therapy and treatment as it was intended.

Indian Head Massage (or ***Champissage*** as it is traditionally called) is based on a system of healing known as the 'Ayurvedic' system. Roughly translated Ayurveda can be composed of 'life' (ayus) and 'science' (veda). It is not surprising therefore that in Champissage we deal with the gentle manipulation of energy channels with the main aim being to release accumulated stress in tissues, muscles and joints of the head, face, neck and shoulders and upper arms. The techniques that are incorporated into this system have been practiced for over a thousand years in India and have provided generations of people with relaxation and healing for many years.

Today, a typical single treatment can last anything from thirty to forty five minutes and instantly relieves stress and tension in many areas along with combating fatigue, helping to alleviate insomnia, headaches, migraine and sinusitis. A whole array of symptoms may be treated and this therapeutic treatment is deeply calming, relaxing, wonderful, gentle, comforting, balancing and leaves clients feeling energised, revitalised, alert and better equipped to deal with everyday life.

IHM can also increase joint mobility and flexibility in the neck, shoulders and surrounding areas. Blood circulation increases, connective tissue relaxes and the whole treatment helps to eliminate accumulated 'toxins' and waste products. The treatment has a powerful effect on three chakras in the throat, head and crown areas and an improved sense of mind, body and spirit awareness may be enjoyed by anybody from any walk of life and at almost any time.

With many people these days, and certainly over the last few decades in what we would call 'westernised' communities, there has been a great shift in our thinking when it comes to treating symptoms. Much of our new found approach now centres round dealing *with* or treating the *whole person* in a very 'holistic' manner. This has been welcomed by many in society and instead of simply treating any symptoms which may be present the growing trend has been to focus on the person as an individual thereby allowing the possibility of discovering the true *cause* of why a situation or particular symptom has manifested.

Twenty years ago, when I was first studying Swedish Massage for the whole body, which I am now qualified to teach under the **ITEC** system (International Therapist Examination Council), there was still a good amount of resistance to the belief that massage, in *any* form, could be as beneficial as indeed we now know it can be. Whilst it was agreed or even partly assumed that there could be benefits of a holistic 'hands on' approach to healing, symptoms or simply general relaxation, there was still a great reluctance by many, including doctors and health care professionals, to accept fully the role of massage as a credible practice which could deliver beneficial results.

The History of Indian Head Massage

Indian Head Massage was first introduced to Western society in the 1970's by a man called **Narendra Mehta** who was blind from early childhood. Narendra is an Osteopath, Physiotherapist and Massage Therapist. He came to London, England to study Physiotherapy during the 1970's and was surprised to learn that head massage in any form was not given as part of the treatment when visiting a barber's shop.

Upon his return to India he researched different forms of head massage in different regions and discovered the methods being used would vary from individual to individual. Barbers might 'treat' his scalp, while females may focus on treating the hair. For added confusion, each person and region seemed to have their own technique individual to them.

Using his wide research, Narendra quickly developed a unique set of movements and introduced them as an easy to follow system that we know, cherish and practice today. Best of all, there really is no right or wrong treatment with IHM as each therapist applies the movements from client to client depending on specific needs.

The Role of Indian Head Massage

Indian Head Massage is very good at tackling and alleviating stress in everyday life and especially in the workplace. ***Stress at work carries a considerable cost*** which can total billions financially and cause major and minor health issues for billions of employees around the world and can affect anyone at any time. Stress materialises in many ways.

- **Repetitive Strain Injury (RSI)**

- **Headaches**

- **Migraines**

- **Joint, shoulder, back and neck stiffness and pain**

- **Eye-strain**

- **Mental tiredness**

- **Depression**

- **Lethargy**

- **Tinnitus**

- **Insomnia**

- **Sinusitis and Congestion**

Whilst it is true that Indian Head Massage is not a cure for the above symptoms, the techniques and whole treatment may alleviate much of the stress and suffering which may accompany the above conditions.

As we all know, any treatment which brings about a good sense of calm and relaxation can truly help to focus our minds away from the everyday distractions of work, life and stress. Often, simply by having the treatment administered we can become more relaxed, stress-free and alert with the ability to concentrate at a much deeper level. We become confident, charismatic and can communicate and listen more effectively.

However stress is manifested to us as human beings, Indian Head Massage can tackle our physical issues directly and as a result helps us to function better on a daily basis. Obviously each treatment is different just as each human being is different and unique with our own set of issues to face. Fortunately, the many forms of massage have been known to humankind for centuries and they have been practiced and passed down the generations for all to share. The beneficial effects are self-evident and massage is now part of our everyday activity found on almost every modern day high street. The real beauty of 'head massage' is that you can perform it almost anywhere from work or in a professional salon, barber's shop or at home.

Summary

Indian Head Massage is traditionally known as *Champissage*

Indian Head Massage was first introduced to Western society by *Narendra Mehta*

Stress at work carries a considerable cost which can total billions financially

Two

The Benefits

Down to Business

Creating Space

The Use of Oils

The Benefits

The benefits of the treatment are numerous from giving a deep sense of relaxation to promoting a greater sense of self-confidence and the effects can be instantaneous. It is an invigorating and refreshing experience which can be enjoyed time and again. A 'balanced' feeling usually ensues and a client feels peaceful and calm. The treatment can help restore the natural healing process as can all 'holistic' therapies which aim to treat the 'whole' person instead of simply treating the symptoms.

By treating the whole person, a client can feel 'in tune' with his or her surroundings and more connected to positive energy as a result.

Positive effects are listed below:

- **Improved blood circulation to the brain promotes clear thinking**
- **Release of tension**
- **Toxins are released from muscles**

- **Deep breathing supplies oxygen to the body**

- **Calm sense of peace and tranquillity**

- **Deep sense of relaxation**

- **Increased energy level**

- **Releases negative energy**

- **Releases anxiety**

Following any treatment which comes in *'hands on'* therapeutic form, along with the many good benefits, clients may also experience other effects. As a result of becoming relaxed, and for a substantial amount of time, clients may experience tiredness in the form of deep relaxation or needing to sleep. In some cases, dizziness may occur, aching muscles and in many instances an increased desire to urinate (as the body will still be eliminating toxins and waste materials for some time after the treatment) which is natural in these circumstances. Usually, side effects will last for a few hours only and it is after this shift has taken place that clients should experience increased levels of energy and improved alertness.

Down to Business

As we approach the learning of any new skill, especially one as valuable and worthwhile as Indian Head Massage, it is necessary to take into consideration not only what we are learning but also why we are learning it and how we intend to use our newly gained skills.

- **Do you intend to offer treatments to friends and family?**
- **Do you wish to study further and offer professional treatments?**

Whatever it is that motivates an individual to decide to learn a complementary therapy, whether it is full body massage, Aromatherapy or in this case Indian Head Massage, this reason should be given the respect it deserves from the outset. If the reason for learning is simply to satisfy a 'passing interest' and to gain a basic knowledge of the subject then this should still be viewed in the same context as if a person was intending to gain a qualification, set up in business and offer professional treatments.

All in all, the therapy itself does not change and neither should our respect and approach to it change either therefore by far the most significant thing to remember about the therapy is that it is always the *treatment that is the most important factor*.

Creating Space

If we were to build a treatment room with the sole purpose of using it as such, there would be two main ways this could be set out or styled. We could make it look either *'clinical'* or *'spa'* in nature.

Obviously, each style of room should be clean, inspire relaxation, be comfortable etc., but depending on the clientele, each of the above factors will be prioritised to a different degree, for example; there is clearly less need to inspire relaxation with burning incense and calming music in an Osteopath's treatment room. Similarly, a relaxing water feature may be unnecessary in a Chiropractor's working space.

However, a mixture of the two styles may be mixed and matched depending on the needs of the practitioner and client. In order to optimise the experience for the person receiving a treatment, it is important to note certain key factors which would naturally appeal to the five senses: touch, taste, smell, hearing, and sight.

A good way to do this is to imagine what you would prefer yourself if you were to receive a treatment.

Think about the following for a moment:

• **How would you react if the room was too cold or too hot?**

• **Would you prefer heavy rock music as opposed to background 'healing' music?**

• **What would you think if the room was unclean and littered with old towels?**

These are not difficult questions to answer and the list could go on but they are incredibly important when thinking of the 'whole' experience which begins the moment a client enters the space. The real key to getting it right is to guide *yourself* through the whole process from beginning to end. Treat yourself as the client and this will help you to succeed in terms of fulfilling their needs. A client arrives, rightly so, with expectations of professionalism which is not surprising and nor is this responsibility to be taken lightly.

The most important single factor which distinguishes a professional as such is their approach to the whole experience from a client's point of view. In this display the client should be made to feel special and this should continue at all times. In short, the attention needs to be focussed on the person receiving the treatment from beginning to end. It starts with the client and ends with the client; *the whole experience is about them and for them.*

As we have seen, there are many things to consider when setting up a treatment space. The best thing is to keep it simple. Make the treatment area as welcoming as possible with a moderate temperature. Along with offering a wonderful experience on a client's first visit, we should always keep another aim in the back of our minds; the aim to make a person feel so welcome and special that they want to return.

Once again, from beginning to end, think of how *you* would enjoy the treatment. You may want a glass of water before or afterwards. You would certainly prefer to hang your jacket as opposed to throwing it on a chair and you would like a mirror to check your appearance upon leaving.

To enhance your space further, you may wish to introduce the following:

Mirror	Water feature	Coat hangers
Good lighting	Incense	Candles
Music	Refreshments	Disabled friendly features

Lastly, as the person offering the treatment, it is important to remember that once your attention is focussed on your client it should remain there.

In other words, once begun, the treatment should not be interrupted. For this to happen, you must be relaxed and ready to perform the treatment. Overall, the key factors to work with are ones that naturally help to create and maintain a good sense of relaxation with a welcoming atmosphere. This is not only important for the person who is receiving the treatment but it is also beneficial to the therapist or practitioner who should be able to enjoy the treatment just as much as the client. The treatment area should be built around certain key principles:

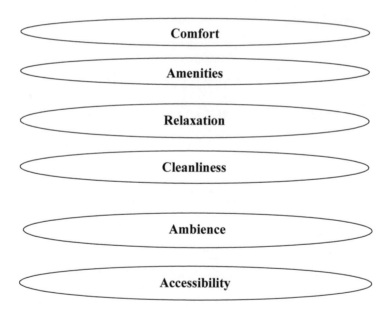

Comfort

Amenities

Relaxation

Cleanliness

Ambience

Accessibility

The Use of Oil

It is personal preference that comes into play when we think about using oils whilst performing Indian Head Massage techniques. As the treatment itself can be very effective often making people feel tired, very relaxed and with a sense of deep euphoria, the use of oils should really be judged wisely and with caution simply because the nature of the oil itself and the function it is supposed to fulfil may be heightened. Using a few drops of lavender oil may seem like a good thing to do if a friend or client has driven over to see you but with the effect of lavender intended to enhance the possibility of sleep, the use of it on this occasion may not be the wisest thing with a return car journey for your client. Naturally this may be different if a client is being treated at home and will retire to bed shortly after receiving the treatment. Personally, I choose not to use oil for a variety of reasons including that their use requires a good knowledge for proper application, they may be messy for the client, the increased effects as explained above and the possibility of allergic reaction.

Summary

By treating *the whole person*, a client can feel connected to positive energy

A treatment area can be either *'clinical'* or *'spa'* in nature

Imagine what *you would prefer* if you were to have a treatment

Make the treatment area as *welcoming* as possible

Three

The Head

The Skeletal System

Systems of the Body

Contra-indications and Conditions

Preparation and Check List

The Head

Typically, the human head is made up of twenty nine bones which consist of fourteen 'facial' bones (front), eight 'cranial' bones (top), six osiccle (ears) and one hyoid (throat).

Cranial Bones

Ethmoid (1)

Occiptal (1)

Frontal (1)

Parietal (2)

Sphenoid (1)

Temporal (2)

Facial Bones

Inferior Nasal Concha (2)

Mandible (1)

Lacrimal (2)

Maxilla (2)

Nasal (2)

Palatine (2)

Vomer (1)

Zygomatic (2)

The following diagram indicates the main bones of the head. If you are seriously considering training further and gaining a diploma or qualification in 'complementary' therapies, it is recommended that you seek further in-depth knowledge of the body, head and human Anatomy and Physiology. You will find that not only is more knowledge and understanding helpful, a good grounding in theory is compulsory before embarking on the practical side. It is always very tempting to simply 'get stuck in' but the more we understand and appreciate the human body and systems therein, the better we appreciate and work with it for the benefit of all.

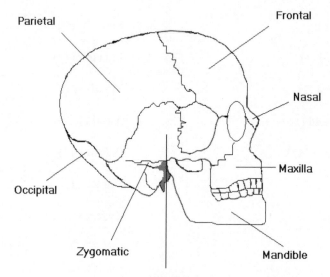

The Skeletal System

Four main functions are attributed to the Skeletal System, described as follows:

- **Protection - skull protects the brain / rib cage protects internal organs**
- **Movement - with the use of the Muscular System bones act as levers**
- **Cell production - bone marrow produces red and white blood cells**
- **Mineral Storage - calcium is a major part of the structure of bones**

The Skeletal System is not instantaneously affected by the effects of Indian Head Massage in the sense that bone does not relax or breathe. However, by becoming relaxed, calmed, and more peaceful with increased blood flow etc. the other biological systems of the human body can be affected immediately or a knock effect can occur.

Systems of the Body

The primary function for each system of the human body is displayed below. Please note that there are definitely other functions also for each system. However, hopefully now a clear connection between all the systems is apparent and with this, it should naturally be easier to see how each system may be affected by the physical application of Indian Head Massage.

VASCULAR – to transport blood around the body

MUSCULAR – to provide movement

ENDOCRINE – to regulate body with hormones

URINARY – to remove waste from the bloodstream

DIGESTIVE – to breakdown food products

LYMPHATIC – absorb and transport fatty acids

CENTRAL NERVOUS – controls voluntary and involuntary bodily functions

SKELETAL – to provide protection

As we should be able to see, with a treatment such as Indian Head Massage that has many beneficial effects, the systems of the human body may be directly affected. Breathing becomes deeper (Respiratory System) allowing us take in larger amounts of oxygen which is transported through the lungs into the blood (Vascular System) which in turns makes us more relaxed. It is with this great sense of euphoria through which hormones are released (Endocrine System). Our muscles relax (Muscular System), Carbon dioxide is breathed out and waste products are produced by our deep sense of relaxation which then enables our Urinary System to work more.

Contra-indications and Conditions

In all forms of massage, there can be a risk to the client if treatment is given where a pre-existing condition is present. A professional approach to all conditions should be adopted at all times. In the physical therapy industry, just as with the medical profession, there are times when treatment should not be given, the therapy should be modified or altered or the treatment should be delayed. Conditions or illnesses which make this so are referred to as *contra-indications.* In instances where a client indicates any *contra-indications* (as listed below) *always* seek the advice and / or permission to perform the treatment by a qualified professional such as their doctor, physician, General Practitioner etc.

This list of contra-indications is not exhaustive. It could contain cancer, lymphatic problems, Multiple Sclerosis, respiratory problems and much more. Migraine is on the list even though IHM may help to alleviate the symptoms. It is common sense to note that with the actual presence of a condition such as migraine *at the time of a treatment* and with the therapy possibly increasing blood flow to the head and surrounding areas then the effects of the treatment may be less than beneficial in this instance; the migraine conditions may become more severe if it is present.

In my early days of training and subsequently performing treatments of full body Swedish Massage, I recall wondering if there was ever a best time to offer a treatment at all with all of the many human conditions. With many years experience I say to people now who are seriously thinking of training in similar therapies that there is one main defining difference between an amateur and a professional despite the obvious training and qualifications. The difference is; *knowing when not to massage.* If there is serious doubt as to whether to administer a treatment, it is better to decline and to advise the client to seek professional medical advice.

Always seek medical advice if in doubt!

<u>Contra-indications</u>

Recent surgery	**Head problem**
Cuts to the treatment area	**Thrombosis**
Scar tissue (less than two years old)	**Presence of alcohol**
High blood pressure	**Pregnancy**
Eczema	**Migraine**
Neck problem	**Low blood pressure**
Concussion	**Presence of drugs**

Preparation and Check List

Before we begin any treatment which is regarded as a complementary therapy and which involves 'one to one' treatment, it is necessary to follow a quick common sense check list. This is important for the main purpose of being able to allow the treatment to continue *uninterrupted* once it has started. There will be many things to consider depending on where and how you will be performing your treatment and on whom but to give yourself the best chance of having another person truly enjoy the effects of what you are doing from beginning to end, then it is advisable to run through both a standard and more personalised check list before you begin. This can be done either mentally or from written notes with *personalised* remarks relating to the person you are treating. (We shall cover the need and importance of confidentiality later).

- **What happens if there is a power cut?**

- **Do you have ice for refreshments?**

- **Is there a First Aid box?**

- **Do you have short and clean fingernails?**

- **Will you be interrupted by a ringing telephone?**

- **Do you have a pet needing attention?**

- **Is the treatment area warm or cold enough?**

- **Do you have ventilation or a fan?**

- **Do you have items close by such as oils, towel, supporting cushion?**

- **Have you checked the comfort of your client?**

There really is a great amount to think about when thinking about offering treatments. Are *you* relaxed with a good posture, clean personal hygiene, no over-powering cologne, sturdy and suitable footwear and much more? The list really is endless and relates more than anything to *allowing* your client, friend or family member to become relaxed and to *enjoy* the treatment.

It is up to you and you only to ensure that your favourite pet is not scratching at the door to enter the room, to make sure that a ringing telephone does not startle you or your client, and to ensure you have ice cubes at the ready for the client who prefers them in a cold refreshing drink either before or after the treatment. Remember to follow a *standard* and *personalised* check list for *each* client.

Summary

A good *grounding in theory* is compulsory before embarking on the practical side

Conditions or illnesses are known as *contra-indications*

Always seek medical advice where *contra-indications* are present

Allow the treatment to continue *uninterrupted* once it started.

Follow a *standard* and *personalised* check list for *each* client

Four

The Treatment

Keeping Fit

Timing the Treatment

*Please note that in the interests of safety or for the reason that the technique would need a greater 'in-depth' explanation which is not possible in this introductory manual, there are a few techniques which the author has chosen to omit.

Extreme care, caution and consideration should be taken at all times when practicing or performing any described techniques. The techniques have been described for the purpose of this introductory manual and in order to provide information.

Any of the techniques or treatments, if administered, shall be offered at the sole discretion of the reader of this material.

It is always wise to check allergies, preferences and any pre-existing medical conditions before the treatment commences.

The Treatment

The client sits upright and relaxed in a comfortable chair. This does not have to be a chair specially designed for the treatment but instead it just has to be comfortable, supportive (to the patient's back and posture) and one in which the patient is allowed to feel relaxed. For this purpose, it is usually best not to use an armchair where possibly only the head is visible and accessible as the working therapist will need to reach and work on the head, neck, shoulders, arms etc. The treatment commences with the therapist using a wonderful range of different movements.

Additionally, the therapist gently stimulates and strokes facial pressure points along with kneading of the neck and shoulders. The whole session lasts from twenty five to forty-five minutes with a five or ten minute post treatment rest once the massage is complete. The patient may be clothed or unclothed from the waist upwards depending on the temperature of the surroundings or treatment area along with their personal preference. Oils may be used, creams or nothing depending on the requirements of the treatment and the personal preference of the client and therapist.

Before you begin, two important questions need to be asked in relation to the possible presence of contra-indications:

- **Should you perform the treatment?**
- **What should you say to them if you decline the treatment?**

Now simply refer back to creating the most suitable surroundings, making a client feel welcome and working from a point of view of how we would like to be treated. Assuming we are offering a treatment at home, we may burn incense, candles and allow gentle ventilation, and relaxing music with no outside distractions such as ringing telephones.

As much as possible, the treatment area should be set up before the client arrives with the emphasis on relaxation at all times and before the treatment begins, the client must be consulted to rule out any contra-indications, allergies, sensitive areas etc. The client should be seated comfortably in a supportive chair, arms resting at their side, without restrictive clothing. (At least two hours after their last meal and no alcohol).

If necessary, feel free to offer a cushion for extra back support. Jewellery around the face, ears and neck should be removed by the client. Similarly, items of our own jewellery should be removed along with bracelets, watches, rings etc. Remember we shall be working closely on gentle areas and care should be taken at all times.

The emphasis now is on your client relaxing. Allow them to use the bathroom, take a refreshing beverage, carefully hang up their jacket etc., and switch off their own telephone. Make it clearly known to your client that you are washing your hands. Leave the room to do so, allowing client privacy, and indicate where they should sit when they are ready to begin. Return to the room to commence the treatment.

Stand directly behind the client. We shall invariably be resting the open palm of one of our hands flatly on their forehead whilst performing a specific step of the treatment with our other hand. Your position should be so that if your client were to stand up, you would be looking directly at the back of their head.

• Brush hair slowly with open hands from forehead to back of head (three times)

• Repeat and brush hands further down to end of both arms (three times)

• Place open palm on client's forehead

• Make small circular 'two second' movements (3 fingers) in areas 1 to 3 (Fig A)

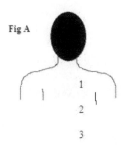

Fig A

- Repeat the above steps two more times
- Swap palm on forehead

- Small circular 'two second' movements (3 fingers) of other hand 1 to 3 (Fig B)

- Repeat steps two more times

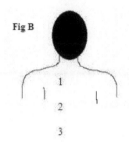

Fig B

- Swap palm on forehead

- Make small circular 'two second' movements (3 fingers) in areas 1 to 2 (Fig C)

- Repeat two more times

- Swap palm on forehead

- Small circular 'two second' movements (other side) in areas 1 to 2 (Fig D)

- Repeat two more times

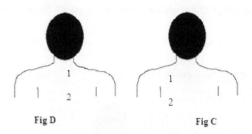

Fig D   Fig C

- Swap palm on forehead

- Roll inside of thumb under ear to end of shoulder with slight

  pressure (Fig E)

- Repeat two more times

- Swap palm on forehead

- Roll inside of thumb in same way on other side (Fig F)

- Repeat two more times

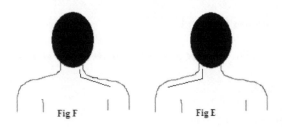

Fig F   Fig E

- Swap palm on forehead

- Repeat movement three times with thumb to half way mark

  with more pressure

- **Swap palm on forehead**

- **Repeat movement three times on other side (half way) with more pressure**

- **Place client's right hand on left shoulder – hold client's right elbow and hold left**

  hand in place on shoulder - roll shoulder joint round forward and back three times

- **Repeat process on other arm**

- **Gently squeeze arms in three places as below – both sides at same time (Fig G)**

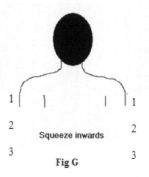

Fig G

- **Squeeze and lift shoulders on either side (at position 1)**

- **Ask client to inhale – ask client to exhale (drop shoulders at same time)**

- Place one open palm on client's forehead

- Thumb circles points 1 to 3 (repeat three times in total) (Fig H)

- Swap palm to forehead

- Thumb circles points 1 to 3 on other side (repeat three times in total) (Fig I)

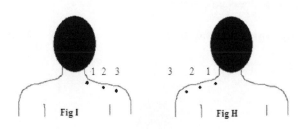

Fig I   Fig H

- Swap palm to forehead

- Lean head to side – if left hand holding – lean head to left side to open other side of neck – thumb circles 1 to 3 (three times in total)

- Swap palm to forehead

- Repeat on other side (three times in total)

- **Use open palms to brush both sides of hair from forehead and down both arms**

- **Palm to forehead**

- **Three fingers 'two second' movements 1 to 3 at occipital bone (ridge) (Fig K)**

- **Repeat two more times**

- **Swap palm to forehead**

- **Three fingers 'two second' movements on other side (Fig J)**

- **Repeat two more times**

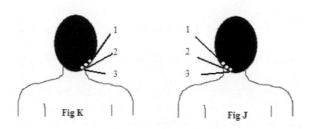

Fig K   Fig J

As you can clearly see by now, there are definite patterns to the treatment and with the preliminary relaxation, shoulder joint mobilisation, stroking and muscle work (thumb circle *petrissage*) now done, the client should be fairly well relaxed and ready to continue. Movements are repeated in two or three places (for example; along the shoulder) and in sets (repeat two more times etc.) meaning the movement may be done nine times in total and then again on the other side with swapping palms to the client's forehead. Resting our palm in such a way allows us to maintain our own good posture, give support to the client and most importantly to hold the client's head as much as possible. It is head massage after all. Having said this, bear in mind that many times, a client will fall to sleep or come very close to it and a human head can be very heavy. *Be forewarned about this as a sleeping client can make the treatment very tiring for the therapist who is constantly holding a client's head.*

Once you are comfortable and confident with using, understanding and applying the techniques, feel free to add an extra set, remove a set and change the order of moves altogether. Also, note from the outset that the client should *never dictate the treatment* and the therapist must always administer the treatment the way they think best. To do this best, you must display a good level of confidence. If you forget a move, then move on and do something else.

Change the order but keep going; *the client will never know.*

An important golden rule with massage of most forms is that (I have certainly seen this myself), as soon as the treatment has begun and the therapist has placed the first hand or finger on the client then *contact must be maintained* until the end of the treatment. Common sense dictates that this adds to a good level of trust. If a client has their eyes closed in a deep state of relaxation and a therapist is walking around in the background then it stands to reason that this works against the desired outcome. In this way, the client will never be able to relax properly.

Be confident, calm and organised and remember to enjoy the treatment. If you are tense, this tension will be felt and absorbed by the client. If you are calm, your client will follow.

- **Remain standing behind your client**
- **Place one palm on client's forehead**
- **Make soft fist with other hand – open hand to create small letter 'c' shape**
- **With 'c' hand use outside of hand (Karate chop side) gently scrub client's hair using circular movements in zig-zag on one side of skull front to back (Fig L)**

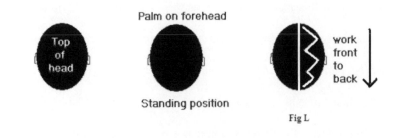

Fig L

- **Swap palm on forehead**

- **Repeat technique on other side(Fig M)**

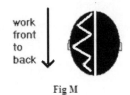

Fig M

- **Swap palm on forehead**

- **Make small three finger circles in same zig-zag pattern**

- **Swap palm on forehead**

- **Make small three finger circles in zig-zag pattern on other side**

- **Gently drum fingertips (both hands) over full area of scalp for thirty seconds**

- Gently run fingers over full area of scalp for thirty seconds (front to back)
- Gently 'pluck' full scalp with both hands for thirty seconds
- Gently 'scrunch' client's hair and scalp between fingers over full scalp – place hand on scalp and try to grab scalp making hair scrunch between fingers – once this happens and hair is gently pulled at roots – release hair – move to another area of scalp
- Remain standing behind client at all times
- Move close as possible to client to support head against your stomach if necessary - apply finger point pressure (middle finger) to points 1 to 3 on both sides at same time – client should close eyes naturally (below)

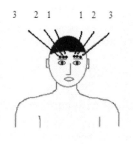

- Repeat moves backwards from points 3 to 1 (both sides at same time)

- Repeat moves again from points 1 to 3 (both sides at same time)

- Apply middle finger gentle pressure under cheek bone on both sides

- Apply middle finger gentle pressure to different points of cheek to ear

- Apply middle finger gentle pressure under jaw bone slowly in different points from ear to under chin – place fingers underneath on both sides - gentle upwards pressure

- Place closed fingers over client's eyes – one hand on either eye for ten seconds

- Press open palm (fingers pointing upwards) over both client's ears to block out noise

- Repeat process of covering eyes then ears two more times each

- One hand under client's chin and one palm under occipital bone with very gentle lift

- Swap hands two times with another gentle lift each time

- Brush client's hair with open hands from front to back three times

- **Brush head again from front all the way down to arms**

- **Lift both client's shoulders – up (client inhales) – gently drop (client exhales)**

- **Ask the client to take three deep breaths and to remain seated for a few moments before moving**

The last step of asking the client to stay seated for a short while is very important as this is the time when they should be feeling the most relaxed, sleepy and perhaps even a little heady or dizzy. Simply inform your client that you will wash your hands then return to the treatment area allowing your client space and time to return to normal.

As the therapist, there are so many different running orders in terms of treatment from beginning to end but it is best to start with general 'opening' techniques, then move to the head and lastly the face returning to general techniques again to 'close' the treatment. The more familiar you become with the many different techniques, the easier it will be to rely on them as 'tools of the trade' flicking easily from one to the next.

As a helpful guideline, instead of thinking or worrying about the whole treatment, simply start performing one technique then decide on the next one before you have finished. This will create a seamless order through which you will become confident and relaxed and your client will be also. Set aside as much time to practice as possible, become familiar with all of the techniques and try to master the running order that suits you and your client best. Know which particular technique you will perform before you perform it.

As I said earlier, whatever you do, do not become worried, stressful or start to panic. Believe me, your physical and emotional stress and tension *will be communicated* to your client, friend, family member or whoever it is who is receiving the treatment. Stay in view of a clearly visible clock, time the treatment, breathe deeply, relax and enjoy the treatment just as much as the person who is receiving it.

Keeping Fit

When performing a treatment we should bear in mind that it is necessary to be fit enough to perform the task in hand from start to finish. This means not only being alert, energetic and physically fit but also having good posture, good stamina, strength and keeping ourselves in the best physical state through which to offer a treatment at any time.

But what does this mean exactly?

Simply, this does not mean that we have to get up at the crack of dawn, start the day with a brisk 10km run followed by a trip to your local gym for a gruelling workout. But it *does* mean that we should attempt to keep ourselves in a good state of being and health so that we may spring into action at the drop of a hat. Whether you intend to train further and to turn professional or simply offer relaxing treatments to friends and family, you need to take good care of your body and especially your back and hands.

I recall a time many years ago when I had first qualified in Swedish massage and had just begun offering treatments at home. I had recently advertised and was ecstatic at the prospect of having booked in two full body treatments for the following day so much so that I decided to cook my favourite meal that evening and in the process managed to make a somewhat nasty (though not debilitating) cut to my left thumb. Naturally, this had not healed by the next day but I was adamant that I should not cancel. The treatments were a great success despite not having full use of one my most important digits when it comes to an hour long massage treatment.

Hopefully, from this we can conclude that it is vital to take care of our bodies, to look after our health, our daily posture, and even adapt our lifestyle and habits to some degree in order to remain in a state of readiness.

Timing the Treatment

Time will fly especially when you are enjoying what you are doing. However, if you are 'professional', time is money and this is something that should be monitored. If you are working towards a forty five minute treatment in total try to allow enough time for each move on each side in each section. If this is not possible, then miss a movement and go to the next one.

Clients need to feel like you are in control. Essentially, timing is something that you learn only by performing treatments and by getting the timing wrong but eventually you should be able to perform a whole treatment without feeling the need to even use a timing device; *your treatments should feel natural.*

Relax and think about a beginning, middle and end and in time things should run smoothly and seamlessly.

Summary

Check for *allergies, preferences* and any *pre-existing medical conditions* before the treatment commences.

No *alcohol* or *food* consumed at least *two hours* before treatment

Look after yourself and remain in a *state of readiness* to offer treatments

Stress and tension *will be communicated* to your client.

Five

The Common Code

Professionalism

Ethics

Client Cards

Data Protection

The Common Code

With any profession there is usually a set of guidelines or rules by which to work and Indian Head Massage is no exception. A professional approach is necessary from the outset irrespective of whether or not we are offering a free treatment or will receive payment in return. In the interests of all complementary therapies, it is important to foster good relations between the many different professions. Whether your path crosses with another therapist in a working or friendly way, you should always remember that a lot of training, study time and dedication to a particular subject is involved and through any possible differences in therapies being offered, there is also a common code that binds us together.

Professionalism

As a therapist, we must always maintain a professional approach towards clients. By this we can assume that 'professional' includes the following:

1. Respectful – civil, polite, well-mannered

2. Welcoming – treat all people equally

3. Honesty – offer fair treatment to match the individual

4. Discretion – do not disclose client's issues to third parties

The main points above are really quite standard to any profession and essentially are also common sense behaviour. But do not be tempted to underplay these points. For example; it is wise to be **respectful** and **welcoming** in your approach so that your client enjoys the experience and is left with a good inclination to return. Be **honest** with the treatment; do not offer a 'standard' treatment which you have learned and could apply to anyone. Instead, be specific to the client and fair to their needs and expectations tailoring the treatment to the individual.

Discretion is extremely important in terms of a client being able to trust a therapist and also because in most instances it is a legal requirement not to disclose medical conditions, personal information etc. to third parties.

Once again, to think in terms of a client's needs it is advisable to gauge what *we* would like as individuals if we were to receive a treatment. An individual should be allowed to talk openly and act freely in order to relax.

Remember to treat your client how you would expect to be treated.

Ethics

As we can see, handling clients in a professional way is extremely important. It not only allows you as a therapist to act and perform a treatment with an air of authority, it also gives clients a definite expectation of how they will be treated. A clear line can be drawn which distinguishes therapist and client. Some common guidelines which are upheld throughout the therapy industry can be noted below which help both therapists and clients to establish and maintain a good working relationship.

- **Professional conduct towards all clients and other therapist at all times**
- **Respect different Laws and Customs**

- **Seek medical permission to perform treatments with contra-indications**

- **Do not treat another therapist's client without the therapist's permission**

- **Do not diagnose any symptoms or recommend treatment or cures**

(An important factor to note with regards to the last point above is that in all circumstances only people with full proper medical qualifications are allowed to diagnose or treat on a medical basis)

Obviously, this list of guidelines is not exhaustive but what it does hopefully is that it helps to establish a platform of honourable standards on which appropriate behaviour can exist and which allows acceptable practices between therapist and client.

Client Cards

Unless you have a super 'turbo-charged' memory with which you are able to remember everything about a person, it is wise to keep a client record card. This can be done as either part of a card / index system, in the form of a journal or whichever way you find most suitable.

Name	
Address	Telephone number
Contra-indications	Likes / Dislikes / allergies

Date of Birth	Treatment given
Treatment date	

If you are using a card system, the client slip should include basic 'common sense' information such as given below. There is no need to overcrowd it but do remember at all times that all information supplied should remain private and confidential especially information which relates to medical conditions. This is not only polite; it can be illegal to impart personal information to third parties.

(Please see the earlier typical example of a client card)

Data Protection

There are very distinct laws governing the collection and use of personal data and it is in the interest of all that these guidelines are observed. If you are hoping to set up in business, after further training, then it is advisable to familiarise yourself with the basic principles of the Data Protection Act in case the instructions therein are or do become applicable to your working practice. The basic premise of the act (certainly in the United Kingdom where I have performed treatments), is that any person or company who intends to hold personal information (data) on other individuals (subjects) is required to exercise a good level of responsibility towards the gathering, holding and storing of such data. This applies to storage on computer systems (electronic means) and may apply also to written storage such as client cards. These can be legal requirements especially where sensitive data such as medical information is gathered. It is wise to check with the appropriate departments in all cases in order to comply with requirements.

Summary

Remember to treat your client how *you would expect* to be treated

Do not diagnose any symptoms or recommend treatment or cures

Familiarise yourself with the *basic principles* of data protection

Six

Return Custom

Advertising

Insurance

Return Custom

With all that has been said so far, apart from my own personal hope that you may wish to seek out further learning through a professional DVD, a Diploma course, insurance, practical training and all that goes with it, there is one thing that you will need above else *if* you are thinking of *'turning professional'* and offering treatments in some way, shape or form; *clients.*

As I said much earlier, one of the important things to do with clients is get them to return and return to you as opposed to another therapist. This does not mean that we steal clients from other working therapists; it simply means that when a client comes to you for the first time you must do all you can to make them return without forcing them. We can do this by getting to know them in the short space of time that we have with them.

Obviously, throughout a treatment we do not strike off conversations but in the time we spend with a client, we must remember their likes, dislikes, preferences such as a cushion to sit on, their favourite oil, scent, beverage on arrival, allergies, where they live and so on. The more we know about a person, the more special they will feel as a result. Remember that the 'whole' experience begins the moment a client enters the space. But their memory of you as a therapist and their likelihood of returning to you will last for a long time after their departure.

Do not underestimate your effect on a client!

Advertising

As a professional therapist or practitioner, offering your services can be done in various ways from a simple advertisement in a local newspaper to a 'full on' leafleting campaign operating door to door in your neighbourhood.

However you decide to get knowledge of your services over to other people, there are a few basic things to remember when putting together a suitable advertisement:

- **Type of treatment**

- **Benefits of treatment**

- **Basic contact details**

- **Location**

It is a natural temptation to become tempted to include a huge amount of information which would be totally unnecessary. ***Keep it simple*** with the emphasis on grabbing attention in a very short space of time. The information would be much the same if you were to advertise in a newspaper, monthly journal or pop a postcard type flier through the door of a potential client's home or on a health store notice board.

Be specific about the treatment you are offering in order to establish initial interest for people who either know about such a therapy or may be thinking about receiving a treatment from you for the first time. Clearly state the benefits of the treatment but do not guarantee anything even if guarantees *can* be offered. Remember that each individual is different and whilst *'guaranteed relaxation from stress'* may be seen in some cases, the only other guarantee that come with this is that it will ***not be seen*** in all cases. Basic contact and location details are common sense requirements so that a client is able to contact you. Give general location such as, *'centre of town'*, *'relaxing surroundings'* etc. However, do not be tempted to supply your full address or an endless list of telephone numbers so that you can be reached constantly twenty four hours. As with any business, you will need to attract clients to your services but you will also need to be able to *'switch off'* from the work you are doing.

One of the best ways to do this is to offer limited contact details, provide a telephone or contact number that can be switched off when the day is done and clearly stipulate the times during which treatments are offered. An example of a simple and effective advertisement would be as follows:

> **Indian Head Massage**
> **Relaxing – calming – therapeutic**
> **Available**
> **10am to 8pm**
> **Monday to Saturday**
> **Centre of 'X' town**
> **Call (name) on 'X' number**
> **30 to 45 minute treatments**

Advertising does not need to be difficult in any way and it is about attracting the right clientele at the right time. There is no need to mention price of treatments as this can be done in a precise and confident way when clients call and arrange an appointment.

Insurance

Much further down the line, (after studying further), deciding to set up in business and upon successfully securing premises at which to offer treatments, then you will need to consider insurance. This covers you in two main ways: *personally* and *publicly.* When you are performing treatments there may be a risk to your clients (contra-indications, allergies, malpractice etc.) and insurance is available to cover you in these circumstances in case a client decides to make a claim against you for whatever reason, which is very rare. You will also need to insure your property and anything you use in your work including the possibility of a client being physically harmed in your premises, falling etc. Also consider that you may need to seek permission from your local neighbourhood authority in order to turn your home (if that's what you intend) into a home which can accommodate therapeutic treatments and you have a great deal to consider. However, do not be put off in any way by any of this as starting up in business should be an existing time for anyone. (*Please note: to gain insurance to administer professional treatments, further training should be a mandatory requirement before insurance is provided*).

Summary

Do not underestimate your effect on a client!

Keep advertising *simple!*

Final Summary

As I said right at the beginning of this book, the aim was to give you a basic step by step understanding into the relaxing and beneficial world of Indian Head Massage or IHM. This can only be properly achieved with your own willingness both as a reader and 'student' who wishes to adopt a professional approach to what essentially may one day soon become your employment, or at least part of it.

The truth is, if an individual wants to learn a subject then this is indeed what will happen from beginning to end and with the original motivation to study, whatever that may be, still intact at the finishing line. How far we continue with our studies in the future, as individual people, is dependent on many factors.

Everybody can benefit from the amazing effects of the simple and effective techniques that have been handed down from generation to generation which involve any complementary therapy based treatment, especially one as worthwhile and beneficial as Indian Head Massage. We can bring joy and happiness to friends, loved ones and the whole family whoever and wherever we are in the world.

Enjoy the journey!

A bit about the author

Stephan Julian Radcliffe was born in the North East of England in a small fishing port town called Hartlepool. He spent the first twenty years of his life there before moving to London to pursue many interests from acting to writing, from Feng Shui to Nutrition picking up Massage and Karate along the way. He has a metaphysical outlook to life and loves meeting people from all walks of life firmly believing that all human beings have something contribute to humankind and to the ever evolving awareness. Stephan has lived close to Brick Lane in Spitalfields, London for over fifteen years which he has found fascinating, exciting and vibrant. He is a great believer in 'Social Entrepreneurship' which is essentially a form of 'ethical business' which can be both profitable and socially responsible at the same time. He is qualified in Feng Shui, Body Language, Nutrition and Diet, Indian Head Massage, a qualified Tutor of Massage and is currently training for his 1st Dan in Shotokan Karate.

If you wish to contact the author please visit **www.sjradcliffe.com**